by **Jayneen Sanders**

illustrated by **Stephanie Fizer Coleman**

How BIG Are Your Worries Little Bear?

A book to help children manage and overcome anxiety, anxious thoughts, stress and fearful situations

How Big Are Your Worries Little Bear?
Educate2Empower Publishing an imprint of
UpLoad Publishing Pty Ltd
Victoria Australia
www.upload.com.au

First published in 2018

Written by Jayneen Sanders
Illustrations by Stephanie Fizer Coleman

Jayneen Sanders asserts her right to be identified as the author of this work.

Stephanie Fizer Coleman asserts her right to be identified as the illustrator of this work.

Designed by Stephanie Spartels, Studio Spartels

ISBN: 9781925089219 (hbk) 9781925089202 (pbk)

A catalogue record for this book is available from the National Library of Australia

Disclaimer: The information in this book is advice only written by the author based on her advocacy in this area, and her experience working with children as a classroom teacher and mother. The information is not meant to be a substitute for professional advice. If you are concerned about a child's behavior seek professional help.

Children should never have to worry.
Their job is to wonder and explore.

J.S.

Little Bear was a
worrier.

He worried about everything.

From early in the morning
until late at night,
he worried.

In the morning, Little Bear worried about **going to school** and all the things that could **go wrong** like not knowing his ABCs.

In the afternoon, he worried about going to **soccer practice** and all the things he **couldn't do** like kicking the ball into the net.

And at night, he worried about the monsters
that might be under his bed, and all the
scary dreams he might have.

Poor Little Bear worried day and night.

"You have to **stop worrying**," said Grandma Pearl.

"**Please** stop worrying, Little Bear," said Grandpa Ted.

"**Little Bear!**" said Auntie Boo Boo in a firm voice, "you must stop worrying!"

But even though everyone told Little Bear not to worry, he worried anyway.

Telling Little Bear not to worry didn't make any difference at all.

His worries never went away.

Early one morning, Little Bear wandered
slowly down the stairs and into the kitchen.

His worries felt so **big** and so **scary**
he could hardly move.

His tummy **tossed** and **turned**,
and he didn't feel like eating breakfast.

"My dear Little Bear," said Mama Bear,
"how big **are** your worries?"

Little Bear didn't say a word. He just stretched
out his arms very wide — very, very wide.

Mama Bear took Little Bear's paw.

"My ears are big and round," she said.
"And big round ears are perfect for listening.
Why don't you tell me all about your worries?"

So Little Bear did.

He told Mama Bear all about school and how
he worried he didn't know his ABCs.
Then he told Mama Bear about soccer practice
and how he couldn't kick the ball into the net.
Lastly, he told Mama Bear about the monsters
under his bed and the scary dreams he had at night.

Little Bear told Mama Bear all about his worries.
He talked for a very, very long time.

Mama Bear listened carefully.
She held Little Bear's paw and
listened to every single worry.

When Little Bear had finished,
   he felt a tiny bit better.

"How big are your worries now?"
   asked Mama Bear.

Little Bear spread out his arms.
He spread them out not nearly
as wide as before.

"When we share our worries with someone who makes us feel safe," said Mama Bear, "they often become smaller."

Mama Bear opened the kitchen drawer.

"I have an idea," she said, brightly.

From the drawer, she took out a box
of rainbow-colored pencils and three
pieces of paper.

"Little Bear," she said, "I want you to draw all your worries. I want you to draw every single one."

So Little Bear did.

"How big are your worries now?" asked Mama Bear.

Little Bear held out his paws. The space between them was as wide as his soccer ball.

"My worries are not nearly as big as before," he said.

"Good!" said Mama Bear.
"When we draw or write about our
worries they often become smaller."
Then she folded the pictures in half and
placed them in her pocket.

The next day at school, Mr Whiskers
asked Little Bear to say his ABCs.

"ABCDEFGHIJKLMNOP

QRSTUVWX..Z," he said.

Little Bear forgot 'Y'!

But he didn't worry.

"Good job," said Mr Whiskers, happily.
"You're nearly there!"

Little Bear smiled.

That afternoon at soccer practice,
Little Bear kicked the ball outside the net.

But he didn't worry.

"Good job," said his coach.
"You're nearly there! Try again."

And Little Bear did.

That night, just before Little Bear jumped into bed, he looked underneath the mattress.

"No monsters here!" he said, happily.

Then he hopped into bed and pulled up the
covers so they sat just under his nose.

"How big are your worries now?" asked Mama Bear.

Little Bear pushed back the covers and held
out his paws. There was no space between.

Mama Bear switched off the light and
kissed Little Bear good night.

"Sleep well, my dear Little Bear," she said.

And Little Bear did.

Discussion Questions for Parents, Caregivers and Educators

The following Discussion Questions are intended as a guide only and can be used to initiate an open and empowering dialogue with your child around general anxiety and/or worrying thoughts. The questions are optional and/or can be explored at different readings. I suggest you allow your child plenty of time to answer the questions, as well as encourage them to ask their own questions around this very important topic. It is equally important that you value their input and listen to their voice. Praise your child's responses and always reassure them.

Pages 4–5
What do you think Little Bear is worried about? Do you sometimes worry? What do you worry about? What do you think Little Bear could do when he feels worried?

Pages 6–7
Why do you think Little Bear was worried about not knowing his ABCs? What sport do you play? What are some things you are really good at?

Pages 8–9
Are there any things that worry you at night? What do you do when you have those 'worry' thoughts and feelings?

Pages 10–11
Do you think telling a person not to worry stops them from worrying? Why do you say that? Where do you think Little Bear's worries live? What can you do if you have worrying thoughts in your head?

Pages 12–13
Why do you think Little Bear's tummy tossed and turned? Why do you think Little Bear stretched out his arms very, very wide?

Pages 14–15
When Little Bear told Mama Bear all about his worries, do you think that might have helped him? Why do you say that? When you are worried, who do you tell? Is that person a good listener? Why do you say that?

Pages 16–17

Was Mama Bear a good listener? Why do you say that? Who shows you kindness? Do you think you are a good listener? Why do you say that?

Pages 18–19

Who makes you feel safe? Could you share your worries with that person? Why do you say that? Do you think sharing your worries with a good listener is helpful? Why do you say that?

Pages 20–21

Little Bear drew all his worries; do you think drawing his worries helped? Why do you say that? Have you ever drawn a picture about a worry you had? Did drawing your worry help? How did it help?

Pages 22–23

How do you think Little Bear is feeling now?

If you had a worrying thought what would you do?

Pages 24–25

Why do you think Little Bear didn't worry about forgetting the Y in his ABCs? Do you think he will know all his ABCs next time? Why do you say that? If we can't do something the first time or we make a mistake, what should we do? If we can't do it the second time, what can we do? That's right! We just keep trying.

Pages 26–27

Why do you think Little Bear didn't worry about missing the net? When he tried again, what happened?

Pages 28–29

How is Little Bear feeling now? Why do you think he is feeling that way?

Are our worries real or are they just thoughts in our heads? If you are ever worried about something, what will you do? Do you think talking about or drawing your worries is a good idea? Why do you say that?

Pages 30–31

Why do you think Little Bear is looking so happy and calm?

Pages 32–33

What is Little Bear dreaming about? Do you think his worries have gone away for good? Why do you say that? If Little Bear has any more worries, how do you think he will manage/stop them?

Extra Hints to Help an Anxious Child

*"Worry never robs tomorrow of its sorrow,
it only saps today of its joy."*
LEO BUSCAGLIA

Take children's anxiety seriously

When a child is anxious it is important not to dismiss their feelings. Take them seriously and reassure the child that you are there for them and they are safe. Give them plenty of time, and listen to their worries with serious intent. If the child is anxious about an event, talk through the process involved, and let them know what will happen after the event.

Use a 'bossy' phrase or phrases

Tell the child they can be as 'bossy' as they like with a worry. They can actually verbalize phrases such as telling the worry to 'Go away!' or say, 'I don't have to listen to you.' Let the child choose a phrase they feel comfortable with. All children are different, but you will come to know what phrases work best with a child to reduce their anxiety.

Explore what anxiety looks like physically

Explain to the child what is actually happening to their brain and to them physically when they are anxious. An excellent children's book on this topic is *Hey Warrior* by Karen Young, published by Little Steps Publishing.

Introduce calming techniques

Introduce mindfulness by encouraging children to be conscious of the here and now (being present), and to try and distance themselves from their worrying thoughts; highlighting that worrying thoughts are exactly that, thoughts only. An analogy you could present is that our anxious thoughts are like clouds covering the sky but we know clouds eventually shift, and blue sky is always behind them. Note: there are a number of books for children on mindfulness but we recommend *Sitting Still Like a Frog: mindfulness exercises for kids and their parents* by Elin Snel. Use yoga stretches and calming techniques such as asking the child to take in three deep breaths and blow them out until their breathing returns to a slower pace.

Slow breathing task

Ask the child to imagine they are holding a hot chocolate. Have them take in a long, slow breath through their nose and count silently 1, 2, 3 ... to smell the delicious hot chocolate. Now say, 'But it is too hot to drink, so breathe out 1, 2, 3, 4, 5 and blow on the drink to cool it down.' Repeat.

Art therapy

Use art therapy such as drawing, painting, creating with clay and sand play with the child. Encourage the child to talk about what they drew/made and how it makes them feel.

Five senses

Use this grounding exercise when a child is feeling overwhelmed. Ask them to name five things they can *see*; four things they can *hear*; three things they can *feel*, for example, their socks on their feet, their hands on their lap; two things they can *smell*; and one thing they can or would like to *taste*.

Physical reassurance

Reassure the child that the feeling will pass and provide them with whatever comfort they need, for example, a hug or just being held for a while. Ask the child to decide what they need. A stress ball (a balloon filled with flour or rice) to play with can also be helpful.

Model your own techniques

Let an anxious child know that you, and in fact all people, feel anxious at times and that they are not alone with this feeling. Share some of your own calming techniques such as slowing your breathing down and counting each breath. Remain positive — reassuring the child that the feeling will pass and they **will** be able to move forward.

Encourage the child to 'have a go'

When anxiety-inducing situations or activities arise, encourage the child subtly to 'have a go'. Acknowledge that you know it is hard for them, and therefore, when they take even one little step forward, praise them for their courage and persistence. Introduce known anxiety-inducing situations slowly and encourage all efforts no matter how small.

Doing something fun

Encourage the child to try to give themselves a break and, if possible, put their worries 'away' for a while, for example, on a metaphorical shelf, and do some 'fun' things that they really enjoy such as playing a game outside, listening to music, reading a book or going to the park.

Try to not 'fix' everything

Children with anxiety in the long term need to learn how to cope with stressful situations and anxious thoughts. As tempting as it might be, as a caring adult, try not to completely take over and 'fix' everything for them. Encourage the child to use their own techniques to quell anxious thoughts.

Make a checklist

Make a personalized checklist outlining all the things that work with a child to help reduce the anxiety so when it comes upon them suddenly, they can refer back to the checklist for some ready solutions.

Remember a time

Ask the child to remember a time when they overcame anxiety, and reinforce how brave and competent they were, and how proud you always are of them. This may help them gain the confidence to overcome this bout of anxiety.

Draw or write a different ending

Drawing or writing about an anxiety is a useful tool as shown in *How Big Are Your Worries Little Bear?* You can also move on from this and have the child draw or write about overcoming the anxiety-inducing situation (or task).

About the Author

Jayneen Sanders (aka Jay Dale) is an experienced teacher, author, and a passionate advocate for providing all children with Body Safety and Respectful Relationships Education. Her children's books cover Body Safety, consent, gender equality, respectful relationships, and social and emotional intelligence. Jayneen believes empowering children from an early age makes for empowered teenagers and adults. She is also Lead Author for the children's literacy series 'Engage Literacy' published by Capstone Classroom, and has written over 100 titles for that series. As a mother of three children, Jayneen has always advocated for their rights and encouraged them to have a voice. Her ongoing passion for the safety and empowerment of children continues today with new manuscripts and additional free-to-download resources always in the wings. Her work can be found at www.e2epublishing.info and on Amazon.

Books by the Same Author

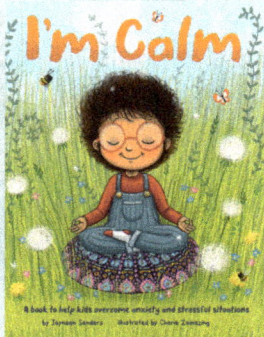

I'm Calm

Theodore is calm. But everyone else in his family isn't! In a time of stress and anxiety, Theodore shows his family ways he's learned to stay calm. Discussion Questions included. Ages 3 to 8 years.

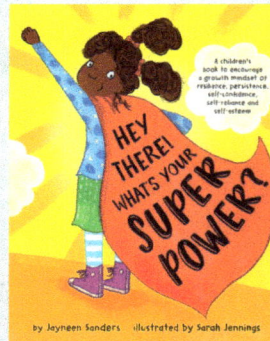

Hey There! What's Your Superpower?

This book provides a number of simple and very achievable 'tasks' to help to kids develop resilience, persistence, self-confidence, self-reliance and self-esteem. Discussion Questions and extra ideas to boost kids' confidence included. Ages 5 to 11 years.

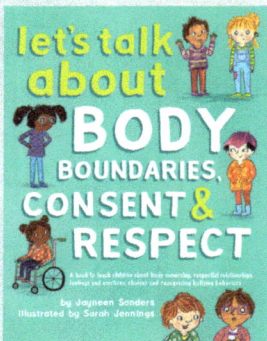

Let's Talk About Body Boundaries, Consent and Respect

Through familiar scenarios, this book opens up crucial conversations with children around body boundaries, consent and respect. Discussion Questions included. Ages 4 to 10 years.

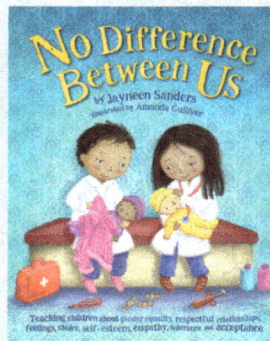

No Difference Between Us

Jess is a girl and Ben is a boy but in all the BIG ways there is no difference between them. A story to explore gender equality, respectful relationships, feelings and self-esteem. Discussion Questions included. Ages 2 to 9 years.

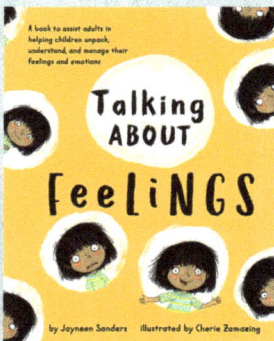

Talking About Feelings

A book to assist adults in helping children unpack, understand and manage their feelings and emotions in an engaging and interactive way. Reader's Notes and Discussion Questions included. Ages 4 to 10 years.

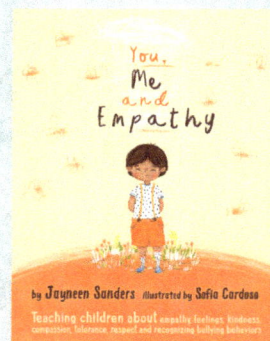

You, Me and Empathy

This charming story uses verse, beautiful illustrations and a little person called Quinn to model the meaning of empathy, kindness and compassion. Discussion Questions, and activities to promote empathy and kindness included. Ages 3 to 9 years.

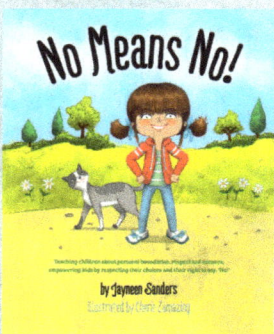

No Means No!

A story about an empowered little girl with a strong voice on all issues, especially those relating to her body! A book to teach children about personal body boundaries, respect and consent. Discussion Questions included. Ages 2 to 9 years.

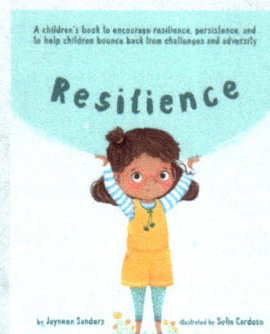

Resilience

This charming story about a little girl called Emmi uses verse and familiar childhood scenarios to encourage children to be resilient, persistent, and to help them bounce back from challenges and adversity. Discussion Questions and activities to promote resilience included. Ages 4 to 9 years.

For more information go to: www.e2epublishing.info

www.ingramcontent.com/pod-product-compliance
Lightning Source LLC
Chambersburg PA
CBHW042143240326
41723CB00013B/580